A boy called Pete

A boy called Pete

A Popjustice Book
Illustrated by David Whittle

First published in Great Britain in 2006 by Friday Books
An imprint of The Friday Project Limited
83 Victoria Street, London SW1H 0HW

www.thefridayproject.co.uk
www.fridaybooks.co.uk

Text © Peter Robinson 2006
Illustrations © David Whittle 2006

ISBN – 10 1 905548 09 5
ISBN – 13 978 1 905548 09 5

British Library Cataloguing in Publication Data

A catalogue record for this book is available
from the British Library

Designed and produced by Staziker Jones
www.stazikerjones.co.uk

The Publisher's policy is to use paper
manufactured from sustainable sources

This book belongs to

_____

I am ____ years old

My favourite Babyshambles
song is _____

When I grow up, I want to be _____

Here is my autograph!

_____

This is Pete.

Pete sings songs and wears hats.

Pete likes to eat lots of special sweets.

Pete also likes to take mountains of mind-bending class A drugs.

Unfortunately, class A drugs are not very good for you.

They make you smelly and a bit untidy-looking.

Once upon a time, Pete was very clever.

He did very well in his exams at school, and was very good at poetry.

He could have gone to a posh school in Oxford, but decided to go to a school in London instead.

When Pete moved to London, he did not have very much money.

But Pete was an enterprising young man – and he set up his own business!

He would kiss men for money.

One day Pete and his friend Carl decided to form a band together.

The band was called The Libertines. The Libertines became very popular.

Pete had a very vivid imagination!

He believed that he was on a boat called Albion.

He thought that the good ship Albion was journeying towards Arcadia – a special place without rules or authority!

Unfortunately, Pete did not live in Arcadia – he lived in London.

London has lots of rules and lots of authority!

The Libertines had many, many fans.

The fans liked the band because Pete and Carl would perform pop concerts in very small places – like their fans' front rooms!

One day Pete decided to put on a special performance in Carl's front room.

The performance consisted of Pete stealing lots of Carl's things.

Carl was very upset. Why would his friend do this?

Pete went to stay in a very big house with high walls.

After Pete's stay in the big house, Carl tried to be friends with him again.

Unfortunately, Pete kept on taking mountains of class A drugs, so Carl had to wave bye-bye to his friend.

This made Pete very sad, so he took some class A drugs and felt better again.

Pete couldn't stop writing brilliant songs, so he formed a new band called Babyshambles who would perform them.

Babyshambles were not very reliable – they kept forgetting to turn up to concerts.

Even their fans found this annoying!

A lady called Dot was very concerned about Pete's behaviour.

She sent him to a special place, far away in Thailand, where there were lots of people who could help him.

Unfortunately, Pete ran away. It was as if he did not want people to help him!

Luckily, Pete met a girl called Kate.

Kate was very famous for being pretty and having her photograph taken.

Suddenly, Pete became even more famous. Everyone was interested in what he did!

One day Kate had a very special photograph taken.

Some people claimed it was a photograph of her snorting a massive line of cocaine up her hooter.

Ouch!

After a while, Pete found that he was not famous for his favourite hobby, singing songs, any more.

Fortunately he found himself a new way to pass the time…

Being arrested!

But Pete didn't like being arrested. He said the police were picking on him.

The police said that if Pete didn't go around with loads of mind-bending drugs in his pocket all the time then they wouldn't arrest him.

Pete did not understand this.

Because he was a sensitive artist, Pete liked to paint pictures.

Sometimes he ran out of red paint, and had to use blood!

Fortunately he didn't paint too many pictures of tomatoes!

So, that's the story of a boy called Pete.

By the time you read this, Pete might be dead!

If he is dead, you should feel very sorry for him because once upon a time he was a very clever and handsome man.

But if he is dead maybe he is happy because it means he is like all of his heroes.

Silly old Pete.

Pete Doherty and his friend Kate are always getting into trouble.

Cut around the edges (be careful with the scissors!) and see what sort of mischief they get up to.

Kate: I am going to the shops. Do you want anything?
Pete: A bag of crack and a Kinder Surprise please.

Have fun!

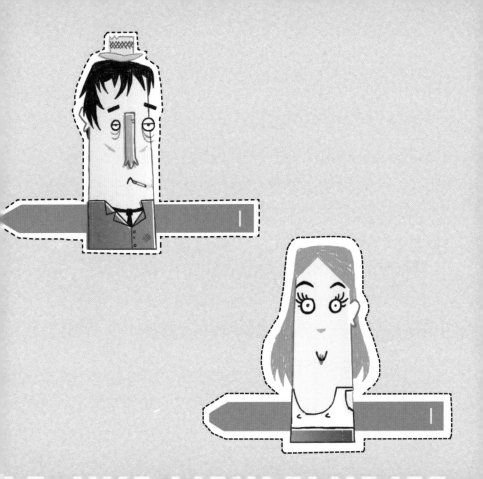

Pop! justice idols

Loads more Popjustice Idols are waiting to say hello to you in your local bookshop - including Robbie Williams, Britney Spears, Eminem, Pete Doherty, Michael Jackson, Elton John, Take That and Madonna!

www.popjustice.com/idols

PLUS!

THE WEBSITE!
Daily updates, podcasts, videos, downloads, pop gossip, pop stuff, pop in general... Plus get Popjustice on your mobile phone!

www.popjustice.com

THE ALBUM!
The greatest pop album of all time, featuring AMAZING songs by AMAZING popstars, all mixed nicely together!

www.popjustice.com/album

THE CLUB NIGHT!
Two floors of unbelievable pop music, every week, in the centre of London town. We do not play stuff by Shayne Ward!

www.popjustice.com/club